Will's first battle

Author
Gill Goddard

Illustrations
David Cuzik

Published by
Scholastic Publications Ltd,
Villiers House,
Clarendon Avenue,
Leamington Spa,
Warwickshire CV32 5PR

© 1994 Scholastic Publications Ltd

Designed using Aldus Pagemaker
Processed by Studio Photoset, Leicester
Printed in Great Britain by Ebenezer Baylis, Worcester
British Library Cataloguing-in-Publication Data
A catalogue record for this book is available from the British Library.

ISBN 0-590-53308-8

All rights reserved. This book is sold subject to the condition that it shall not, by way of trade or otherwise, be lent, hired out or otherwise circulated without the publisher's prior consent in any form of binding or cover other than that in which it is published and without a similar condition, including this condition, being imposed upon the subsequent purchaser.

No part of this publication may be reproduced, stored in a retrieval system, or transmitted, in any form or by any means, electronic, mechanical, photocopying, recording or otherwise, without the prior permission of the publisher.

Picture references
Bodleian Library p18; Bridgeman Art Library p2(top left), Christies Colour Library p15; The Golden Hinde Educational Museum p4(bottom), Michael Holford p2(2nd row right), p9; Mary Rose Trust p2(3rd row left), p6, p8, p17; Museum of London p30; National Maritime Museum p2(2nd row left: William Tyrwhitt-Drake esq), (bottom left), p3, p22(bottom: William Tyrwhitt-Drake esq), p24, p27, p31; National Portrait Gallery p2(top right: 3rd row right), p19, p22(top), p23; Plymouth Marketing Bureau p2(bottom right), p14; Weald and Downland Open Air Museum p13; Zefa p16.

TIMELINE

1534

Henry VIII declares himself Supreme Head of the Church of England. This upsets the leaders of many Catholic countries, particularly Spain.

Henry VIII

1553

Mary Tudor marries Philip of Spain, ignoring the advice of her advisers who warned the Queen that the marriage would be unpopular.

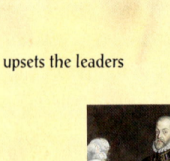

Philip of Spain

1559

After Mary dies, two events make the relationship between England and Spain even more difficult. First, Philip of Spain asks Elizabeth I to marry him but she refuses. Secondly, Spanish ships are regularly attacked and raided by English pirates and adventurers such as Sir Francis Drake and John Hawkins.

1579

Spain gives its support to a Catholic revolt in Ireland.

Elizabeth I

1584

The Spanish ambassador is expelled from England, accused of being involved in a plot to overthrow Elizabeth I.

A ship's compass

1585

To stop the English from helping the Dutch protestants in their revolt against Spain, the Spanish seize some English ships while they are in port.

1586

Francis Drake raids land in the West Indies that is owned by the Spanish. It becomes clear that Elizabeth has given Drake money for his expedition. Philip gets ready to attack England with a fleet of ships.

A ship's cannon

1587

Drake destroys this Spanish fleet at Cadiz.

Sir Francis Drake

1588

February
The English fleet gathers at Plymouth, headed by Lord Howard.

The Armada medal

May
The Spanish Armada sets sail under the leadership of the Duke of Medina Sidonia.

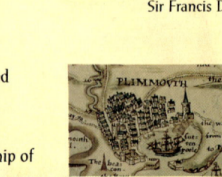

Contemporary map of Plymouth

August
The Armada is defeated in an eight-hour battle near Gravelines and retreats via Scotland and Ireland where it is hit by storms.

WHY DID THE SPANISH ARMADA COME?

During the reigns of the Tudor monarchs, the friendship between England and Spain was constantly under threat. Many of the problems involved religion. While Henry VIII was King, he declared himself Head of the Catholic Church of England and refused to allow the Pope to have any power in his country. The monasteries were closed down and their lands and wealth taken by King Henry. This upset Spain which was a Catholic country.

When Henry's son, Edward, became King, the religion in England became Protestant. Everything changed again when Mary Tudor was crowned in 1553. She was Catholic and wanted England to be Catholic too. She married Philip II, the King of Spain, so for a while the two countries were friends.

When Mary died in 1558 without having any children, her Protestant sister Elizabeth was crowned Queen. The country was Protestant once again. Spain and England were now enemies. Determined to make England Catholic again, Philip tried to help the Catholic Mary Queen of Scots in her plots to take the throne of England from her cousin.

To add to the problems between the two countries, English sea captains, such as Sir Francis Drake and John Hawkins, began interfering with the Spanish transport of gold from its colonies in Central and South America. They attacked the Spanish galleons as they returned home across the Atlantic

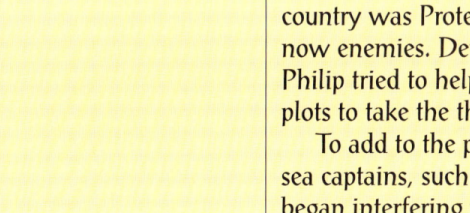

The English and Spanish ships engaged in battle, 1588

and stole their gold. English soldiers were also sent to help Protestant rebels in the Spanish Netherlands from 1585, leading to war between the two countries.

As early as 1582, Philip had started making plans for the invasion of England. When Mary Queen of Scots was executed in February 1587 for plotting to overthrow Queen Elizabeth, Philip stepped up his plans for the invasion. The Armada fleet was built and Philip planned to sail the fleet up to the Netherlands where the Spanish Duke of Parma had a big army ready. The ships were to act as escort to the barges which would bring the Spanish soldiers across the Channel to England. Only Drake's daring raid on Cadiz, which destroyed some of the new Armada fleet, stopped that invasion from taking place that year. However, by May 1588 the Spanish fleet was ready and the invasion began.

1587

Diary of Will Martin, Ship's Boy on the Disdain September 1587 to August 1588

September 6

This is the last night I shall sleep in this house, for tomorrow I shall be at sea with my Uncle Edward on his ship, the Disdain. He is the Ship's Master. We sail for France on the dawn tide with a cargo of wool.

This will be my first voyage as Ship's Boy. I shall keep this journal just like my uncle keeps a ship's log.

I never thought I'd get my chance so soon! I am not even ten, yet I will be a seaman!

I miss my family very much, especially my sister Kate, but I had to leave them to get work. The winter was so bad last year that we would have starved if I hadn't. I was lucky because my uncle said he would take me to work as a servant in his house in Plymouth.

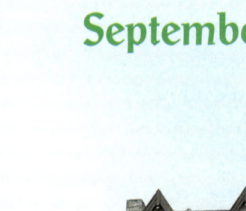

My Uncle Edward lives in a town house like this one in Plymouth.

It was all so strange here at first. The town is so big and busy all the time compared to the farm. I was scared and lonely. I nearly ran back home in the first week because I was so homesick. I've been here now for eight months helping in the kitchen and running errands but now I'm going to do proper work. I've always wanted to be a Ship's Master, not just carrying cargo around the coast but crossing the oceans and fighting battles.

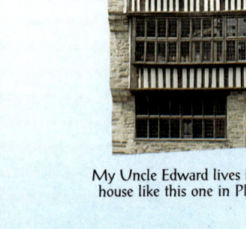

I have always dreamed of crossing the ocean on a ship.

When I first came to Plymouth I begged Uncle Edward to let me start on his ship, but he just kept saying I was too young and I didn't know how hard it would be. He's only taken me on now because his own Ship's Boy died last week. He slipped on the rigging, fell into the harbour and drowned before they could get him out. Uncle Edward needed a new Ship's Boy quickly, so he finally let me take the boy's place.

My uncle told me that I must not call him Uncle Edward but Master when I am on the ship and he said I would be treated just like the rest of the crew. There would be no favours. That scared me a little because he sounded so hard but I'm sure he will take care of me and it will be exciting to sail with him.

1587

September 7

We are about to leave harbour. The Disdain seemed very big when I first saw it, but now I'm on board there is very little room to move. Everything has to be stowed away neatly. It is very difficult to walk from one end of the ship to the other without tripping over something. We sleep below deck and it is dark and smelly down there. The men have to stoop so that they don't bang their heads, but I am small so it's not so bad for me.

September 11

I've been terribly sick for four days now and no one helped me – not even Uncle Edward! They just left me to lie on the deck with a sack over me and a bucket by my side to be sick into. It started soon after we had sailed out of the Sound and the ship started pitching and rolling on the waves. Some of the crew laughed at me but the Master Gunner, Thomas, told me it would pass and I would be alright after a few days. He is the only one who has been kind to me. The First Mate made me drink water every day even though I was sick again soon after. I have had nothing to eat until today when my uncle gave me a hard biscuit which he made me eat, even though I didn't want to. He didn't even ask how I was feeling. No one told me it would be like this. I hope we reach land soon!

1587

September 12

This is a picture of the kind of plates that we use on board ship.

Today I was made to work, even though I was still feeling sick. Harper, the First Mate, took my sack away, made me empty the bucket and told me to start washing down the deck with sea water and a brush. Uncle Edward wasn't on deck at the time so I couldn't tell him I wasn't well enough to work. I felt very weak but I did the job.

One of the men who does the cooking brought me some salt pork and ale when I had finished but it made me feel sick again so I gave it back to him and had a biscuit with some water. Thomas gave me his biscuit to eat too and sat by me to eat his own dinner. He didn't say much, but I felt better with him there.

We had hardly finished eating when the sails seemed to flap and strain at their ties. Everyone seemed to jump up and Harper fired orders to the rest of the crew to lower the sails. Thomas told me later that the wind had changed direction and it would have torn the sails.

Uncle Edward was suddenly there at the helm, steering the ship and giving orders sharply to the Mate, who in turn shouted at the men. Some of the crew were climbing the rigging to take down the big sails in the middle of the ship. Before I knew what was happening, the Mate was dragging me to my feet and shouting at me to climb up to the top of the mainmast with another man. We had to untie the ropes that held the small sail at the top. It was so high and the ship was tossing about in the water so that the mast seemed to lurch from side to side.

1587

I don't know how I got to the top or how I managed to untie the sail ropes but I did. The other man kept shouting to me to tell me what to do. He kept me steady while I loosened the ropes, otherwise I am sure I would have fallen to the deck. I don't remember climbing down but I must have because I found myself sitting with my back pressed against the mast, huddled and shaking. The men just moved around me as if I wasn't there.

Eventually, Thomas came over and put a sack across my shoulders to keep me warm but he didn't say anything. I know I shall never be able to go up on that rigging again, never!

1587

September 13

I slept with the other men below deck last night. They each have their own bundle of sacking and their place on the wooden under-deck. They keep their belongings in small chests and roll up their bedding each morning. It is very cramped and smelly. Nobody seems to wash or change their clothes. Some of the crew have to stay awake through part of the night and they sleep during the day. Thomas told me that Uncle Edward shares the night watches with the First Mate and the Boatswain. I'm glad I don't have to do the night watch.

When we went up on deck this morning, we found that the wind had dropped during the night.

After we had washed down the deck, Thomas showed me how to climb the rigging safely and balance on the spars. He said I would not be expected to go aloft much yet – but in an emergency, like yesterday, I would have to. Thomas also showed me how to pull up the sail and tie it tightly without losing my balance. He is so sure-footed because he has been sailing all his life. He started just like me, as a Ship's Boy. Now he is a Master Gunner and looks after the four cannon.

It is Thomas' job to look after the ship's cannon.

My hands are raw and cut with the handling of the ropes. Thomas told me to soak them in salt water to harden them but it stung so much I nearly cried.

This afternoon I was sent to help the cook gut the fish and boil it! It's not fair! I might just as well be back at Plymouth working in the kitchen. I'll never get to be a Ship's Master if all I do is wash down the decks and cook!

1587

September 14

We anchored in Calais harbour this afternoon. I helped unload the bales of wool on to the quayside. Uncle Edward went to get paid for delivering the wool and to see about picking up some more goods to take back to England. Before he went off he told me I could go ashore with Thomas and he gave me a penny from my pay to spend in the market.

It felt really strange to walk on land again. It seemed to pitch and roll as if we were still at sea and Thomas had to keep holding me steady. He said it always happened like that after being at sea for a few days. It wore off by the time we got to the market.

I couldn't understand what the people in the market were saying but I managed to buy some bread and cheese to eat. When we got back, we ate our food on deck in the dark. It was wonderful to eat soft bread again instead of those hard biscuits. I forced down some ale. We are each allowed one gallon a day but I can't possibly drink that much.

My Uncle Edward uses a compass like this to steer the Disdain.

Thomas is fast asleep near by and my uncle is in his cabin on deck. I know now what Uncle Edward meant when he said it was hard at sea and it has been very difficult for me. I wondered today if I really did want to be a seaman but I know I do, even if it means doing all the messy jobs for years. I'm going to stick at it and show my uncle that he was right to take me on.

1587

September 15

We loaded a cargo of pottery and wine this morning and set sail for Plymouth on the afternoon tide. So far I have not felt sick, thank God! I couldn't face that again. The Boatswain told me that if he had time he would show me the different types of rope and sail on board and how they are stored. I still have to scrub the deck and help the cook but at least I will be learning some real sailing jobs.

September 19

I learned how to mend a sail today. I'm not very good at stitching yet and I stuck the needle into my fingers twice. It is just as well that my hands have lots of hard skin now. Thomas said it takes years to become a good seaman and much longer to be as good a Ship's Master as my uncle. He says I must be patient and learn things slowly, making sure I do everything really well before I try something new.

I asked him if I could learn how to be a Gunner soon. He was really sharp with me. He said I couldn't and I wasn't even to go near the cannon or the powder. I was cross and kept away from him for the rest of the day.

September 20

This has been the worst day of my life! We sailed into Plymouth Sound this morning. I wanted to go ashore as soon as we docked, but I was made to help with the unloading. By the time we had finished, Uncle Edward had fixed another cargo shipment for London. All of the crew had to stay on board and tidy and restock the ship ready for sailing tomorrow. I couldn't believe that he wasn't going to let me go home with him, but when I asked him he just said no, I was to remain on board like the rest of the crew!

I had to work all day just a few feet from Plymouth quayside. I saw John, the tanner's son, going up onto the Hoe to play with his friends and I longed to go too. I suppose that's why I did it. I couldn't help myself. It was easy, really.

Most of the crew were down below and the First Mate was nowhere to be seen, so I crept down the gang plank and ran as fast as my legs would carry me, up and out into the open spaces of the Hoe.

It didn't take me long to catch up with John and I told him all about my adventures. We chased and fought and teased the man guarding the beacon until I had forgotten all about the ship and my new job. It was only at dusk when the boys went home that I realised I would have to go back.

1587

I crept down to the quayside and hid behind some barrels of ale. It was very dark because there was low cloud hiding the moon. I couldn't see anyone on deck so I quietly climbed on board.

Thomas grabbed me by the scruff of the neck as I climbed aboard. He had seen me disappearing up the street in the afternoon and had covered for me when the First Mate asked where I was. When the crew had finally been allowed to go ashore, Thomas had volunteered to stay on board and keep watch. He had told the First Mate that I was sleeping.

Thomas was so angry with me. He said that we would have both been flogged if my uncle or the First Mate had found out I'd gone. He also said that if I ever disobeyed an order again he would be the first to tell my uncle. He stopped shouting and thrashed me. He told me that I had to stay on the ship for the night.

I feel awful. He really hurt me. I don't understand what was so wrong about what I did. I didn't hurt anybody. No-one need have known. And now Thomas won't be my friend any more. I hate this ship.

1587

September 22

I don't think I can go on. I shall have to run away when we reach London. I was so stiff this morning that I could hardly move. Then I cut my hand when a rope slipped. It still hurts even now.

I couldn't bring myself to look at Thomas all day but the worst thing was when Uncle Edward spoke to me. I was scrubbing down the deck when I realised he was standing next to me. He said that he was surprised that I had chosen to stay on board last night instead of coming home. It was terrible. I couldn't help crying; it was the first time he had spoken to me kindly since I'd started the job. He asked me if I was ill. I wanted to explain but Thomas answered for me. He said he had given me a thrashing the night before. My uncle asked him why very sharply and it made me frightened. Thomas made up some lie about me going into the powder room without his permission and my uncle gave me a fierce glare!

November 28

We've been stuck in Cherbourg for five days waiting for the gales to die down so that we can cross back to Plymouth. I have just read my journal and I can't believe I was so stupid. I've done a lot of growing up over the last two months. Thomas would laugh if he knew what I had written. We were friends again within the week, without any words at all.

1587

We are making less trips now that winter has started and Thomas says we all get a holiday over Christmas. I expect I will go home with Uncle Edward. It will be good to get back to a warm place by the fire and good food. I shall have dry clothes at last. I don't think I've been completely dry for weeks now and two of the men have bad coughs because of it.

It's been hard sailing too. The weather is so bad, sometimes I thought we would not make it to a safe harbour, but Thomas was right, Uncle Edward is a really good seaman and he seems to be able to sail us through any storm safely. We still don't talk a lot but I don't mind. At sea he is my Master. At home he is my uncle. It is simple.

December 23

We docked in Plymouth harbour last night and we have spent the day tidying the ship. Thomas' family are all dead so he is staying on board to look after the ship over the holiday. I said I'd go and see him as often as I could. We were paid today. I now have 15 shillings, but half of this is going to my family to help them through the winter. It is the first money I have ever had that is my own.

It is so nice to sit by a fire again, keeping warm and dry.

I am in front of the kitchen fire, warm and full of lovely food. I have always loved Christmas time, even at home when things were so hard. Two whole weeks here before I have to go back on board. I am going to enjoy them!

1587

December 24

I went to the market with cook today to get the food for Christmas. She bought some meat, vegetables, honey, oil and some very expensive spices from a Venetian merchant. He had a little monkey on his shoulder, which was dressed in a doublet and hose. It was very funny to watch.

Plymouth market is not as big as the London markets, but it has a lot of foreign trade and you can get almost anything here. I bought presents for everyone, including Thomas and my own family. I hope I will be allowed to go and see them before we sail again.

December 25

This is a map of Plymouth where I now live.

Today is the feast of Our Lord's Birth. We all went to St Andrew's Church this morning, even Uncle Edward! It was a long service and we got cold standing still for so long. I picked up little Martha because she was crying. Holding her made me remember Jayne and Kate and Edmund at home in Tavistock. I felt really homesick again. I prayed for them all.

After the service I asked Uncle Edward if I could visit my family soon and he said we would both ride out on Twelfth Night to see them!

December 31

I went to see Thomas today. Uncle Edward has asked him to come to our Twelfth Night feast and he said yes. I gave him my present early because it was a new linen shirt and I thought he could wear it for the feast. I think he liked it.

1588

January 5

This wine bottle is made from Delft pottery which is very popular at the moment.

Today Uncle Edward and I rode to my home in Tavistock. We set out at dawn and arrived by noon. I cannot say who was the happiest, my family or me. We hugged and hugged and mother cried. Uncle Edward had brought a basket of food and wine and presents for everybody. It was wonderful to sit at the kitchen table and eat with my family again. After dinner I played with the children in the barn.

We couldn't stay long because we had to get back before it got dark. I gave my presents out just before we left. Father accepted the money with a nod and then he held me tight for a moment before walking back into the house. I got on the horse and waved goodbye. I had to swallow hard to stop myself from crying. We rode back in silence.

There was a splendid feast waiting for us when we got back to Plymouth. Thomas came and we all got presents. Uncle Edward gave me a real dagger with jewels in the horn handle. He said he took it from a Spanish soldier at Cadiz and it is mine now. Thomas gave me a leather belt with ships burned into the leather. It has a buckle in the shape of a ship as well. I was very pleased. We go on board again tomorrow. I hope I won't be sick again!

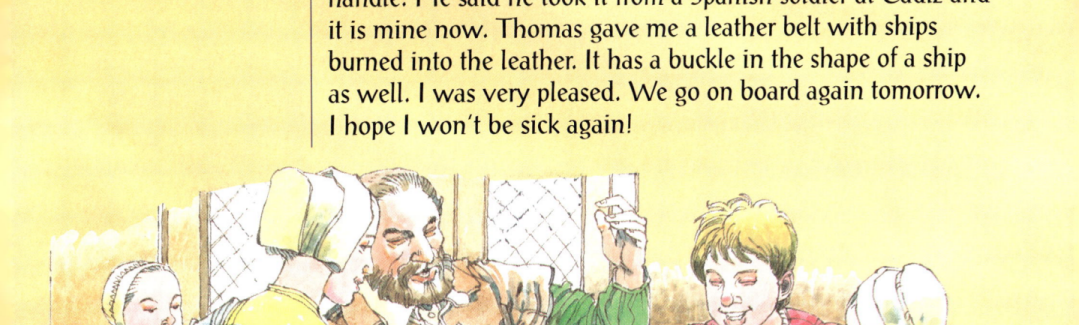

January 18

We finally set sail this afternoon. Bad weather caused a delay. We are making our way around the Cornish coast towards Bristol and then on across the Irish Sea to Dublin. The weather is still bad and I've started to wear a sack over my clothes to try and keep out the worst of the rain. It's very cold and climbing the rigging is dangerous. Uncle Edward warned us all to be very careful. He threatened to flog any one he saw being careless. Thomas told me that my uncle would carry out his threat if he thought it would stop someone from losing their life. I didn't need telling.

1588

January 28

This is Land's End where the storm hit us.

I didn't think any of us would live to see the port of Bristol. The trouble started when a terrible storm hit us as we rounded Land's End. In the middle of the night we were all shaken from our beds by the First Mate with orders to lower the sails. The rain was driving head on into us. I was on deck helping to haul the topsail down when the rope snagged high up. Without waiting to be told, I started up the rigging to free it.

I battled my way in the darkness up the rigging. It was difficult to keep my footing but I struggled up to the top. My knuckles were white as I gripped on to the ropes above me.

The ship was almost out of control, pitching and rolling in all directions. As I glanced below, I saw Uncle Edward fighting to hold on to the helm against the enormous waves that roared around us. I had edged my way along the spar and freed the sail rope when a terrifying flash of lightning seared out of the darkness. It struck the mainmast about two yards below me. I was blinded by the light and clutched tightly to the spar. I heard a terrible crack and the mast snapped in two, with me on it. I fell with the spar but the side rigging stopped it from crashing to the deck. Instead it hung, drooping down and swinging dangerously in the high wind. I found myself hanging by my arms. My body and legs were swinging and twisting in the wind. I must have screamed but no sound came out. My hands were slipping from the wet canvas. I thought I was going to die.

1588

A powerful voice out of nowhere ordered me to hold on. It jolted me back into trying. I tried to tighten my hold. Suddenly, I felt a metal hook catch into my leather belt. Then the spar I was hanging on to was being pulled towards the side rigging. My arms went numb and I fell.

It was over in a second. I did fall but only a few inches into the side rigging and into the strong body of Thomas. He gripped me tight around the waist as the hook was taken off by someone else. It was only then, as I clung to Thomas, that I realised that my uncle was also up there. Both of them were balanced dangerously on the narrow side rigging. I was back down on deck before I knew it. My uncle was back at the helm and Thomas carried me below to my bedding and left me to rest.

Uncle Edward's flask

It was hours before I had enough strength to get out of my wet clothes and under the covers. I couldn't stop trembling and I was very cold. I sat up and hugged myself to try and get warm. I closed my eyes and when I opened them Uncle Edward was crouching alongside me. He looked grey with exhaustion. He held a small flask to my lips and helped me to drink some of the burning drink. It made me choke but as it went down it seemed to light a fire inside me. I took a few more sips and then he took it back. He took a mouthful himself, ruffled my wet hair and got stiffly to his feet to go back on deck.

It took us three days to reach the safety of Bristol harbour and all through that time my uncle stayed at the helm. Only he could have kept the ship afloat in such awful weather with that damage. I shall never forget it as long as I live.

1588

March 29

It was good to sail back into Plymouth again. The ship was taking in a lot of water on the way home and I had to pump it out of the bottom of the hold using a long iron pump. It made my back and arms ache and I got very tired. The ship will stay at Plymouth for two weeks so that the hull can be checked for holes. Thomas will stay on board again and I am to go back to my aunt's.

April 5

There are a lot of soldiers in the town and some of the naval ships have arrived in the harbour. Everyone is talking about a Spanish invasion. I don't know what is going on but the people in the town all seem to be edgy. My friend John is going to meet me at the market tomorrow if his father lets him off work. We are going up to the Hoe.

April 6

The soldiers at the market looked like this. This man is Martin Frobisher, a famous adventurer who is a friend of the Queen.

Something happened today and I am not sure if it is even safe for me to write it down. When I got to the market cross to meet John, lots of soldiers were stopping and searching all the merchants and townsfolk. One of the soldiers grabbed hold of me and searched me! He was very rough and he wouldn't tell me what he was looking for, which made me very angry. John told me that he had been searched too as he came up Market Street. Suddenly a scuffle broke out behind us and two or three men were dragged off by the soldiers. I knew them. They were brothers and they owned a farm just outside the town. Each week, they brought their eggs and cheese in to the market to be sold. Cook had often bought food from them. It was really scary. John told me that the soldiers thought that the two men were spies and that they would be tortured until they confessed to giving away our country's secrets to the Spanish. They would be hanged for treason, up on Plymouth Hoe. Now I am more afraid of our own soldiers than I am of the Spanish.

1588

April 9

A picture of Sir Francis Drake, who is coming to my Uncle Edward's house.

The house is in chaos today. Cook told me that the great Sir Francis Drake was to visit Uncle Edward and stay to supper. I had to help clean the house from attic to cellar and cook spent ages making the supper. I was really excited about seeing him. He is so famous. He has sailed all the way round the world and last year Uncle Edward sailed with him when he attacked and burned the Spanish Armada at Cadiz.

I was disappointed at first – he was smaller than I thought he would be and he looked quite ordinary, although his clothes were richer than my uncle's.

He had a small beard and his hair was brown and curly. But I soon realised that size means nothing – he is a powerful man and I would do anything for him!

After I had helped my aunt to serve the meal, I was allowed to stay in the parlour in case they wanted more ale. I sat on a stool in the corner and was very quiet so that I could hear what they were saying. Sir Francis Drake wants my uncle to help him fight the Spanish when the new Armada comes. He reckons they will try to attack England before the end of the summer. I thought Uncle Edward would agree straight away. I would have! But he just said he would carry on shipping goods until the attack came and then he would help to stop the Spanish. Drake seemed quite happy with that and shortly after that he left. Just think, in a few weeks time I could be fighting the Spanish!

1588

May 23

One of the crew was flogged today. His name is Butcher and he only joined us two weeks ago. He came back on board last night very drunk and picked a fight with the First Mate. Thomas helped to stop the fight and Butcher was tied up and put down into the cargohold to sleep it off. I thought that would be an end of it but after we had left harbour this morning for London, Uncle Edward had him fetched up on deck. The First Mate had the helm and we were all made to stay on deck and watch.

The man looked grey-faced as he stumbled into the light. He scowled at Uncle Edward as he stood in front of him. Uncle Edward was holding a thick leather whip curled in his hand. He was very calm but his face was hard and it scared me. He told the man that he would not have drunkenness or fighting on his ship and that he would be given 20 strokes of the lash to help him remember that. The man turned even whiter and started to speak but Uncle Edward had already nodded to the two men that held him. They dragged him away to the mainmast. He was shouting and cursing but I could tell he was really frightened. The men tied his wrists around the far side of the mast so that his back was facing us. One of them pulled down his shirt so that he was bare from the waist up.

1588

Uncle Edward stood completely still and his face was like stone. I had never seen him like that, never! I thought he was going to flog the man himself but he threw the whip to Thomas who was standing by me. I looked at Thomas with horror but he didn't seem worried. He just stepped forward, a few paces from the man, and unfurled the whip.

The air cracked as the whip stung the air. The sound mixed with a scream and a trickle of blood fell from a long cut across the man's back. Again the sound came and another cut appeared, though not once had I seen the whip strike. My legs started to shake and I felt myself go dizzy. I knew it was foolish but I had to stop it. I just had to!

I remember rushing forward and throwing myself against the man's back just as the whip cracked again. I felt a burning line cut across my shoulders. I arched my back in pain and slumped to my knees. A rough hand grabbed hold of my hair and yanked me to my feet. I didn't see who it was. I was thrown over to the side of the deck and I hit my head on something. It dazed me and I had to shut my eyes. The terrifying sounds seemed to go on for ever. I buried my head in my hands and tried to shut it all out.

After a while everything stopped and there was movement and the usual noises. No one came near me. I must have sat huddled there for ages. At last I looked up. The man was gone and everything looked normal. I slowly got to my feet, took my bucket and scrubbed down the deck as hard as I could.

I couldn't face my meat and ale at noon. I sat alone by the sail boxes and looked out at the sea.

Later on Thomas came over but I didn't want to speak to him. I don't know how he could have done that. He felt the bump on my head and then lifted my shirt to put some grease on the cut across my shoulders. Then he went away. Why does Uncle Edward have to be so hard? I don't understand.

1588

June 20

This is Philip II, King of Spain.

Home at last! I am always glad to get back to Plymouth. The trip back was very rough. When we sailed into the Sound we had trouble finding a place to dock in the harbour. There are ships everywhere! Drake's ship, the Revenge, is moored with his fleet by St Nicholas Island. His ship is magnificent!

As soon as we tied up, a soldier came aboard with a message for Uncle Edward, who left straight away. When he came back, he called the crew on deck and told us that he had agreed to join the English fleet to fight the Armada. He said that we could leave if we didn't want to fight but no one did, apart from Butcher. We are to pick up supplies of food, water and gunpowder for the cannon tomorrow and Thomas said that there would be four Gunners taken on to help him fire the guns. At last I shall get to fight in a real battle!

June 24

I asked Thomas today why the Spanish wanted to attack us with their ships. He said that he didn't really understand it himself, but that the Spanish and English have been enemies ever since he can remember. He thinks that the King of Spain wants to kill our Queen and take over our country. That's why our ships have to win.

There are rumours that Philip II wants to kill Queen Elizabeth I who is shown here.

1588

July 12

It's been two weeks and still there has been no attack! We have been here in Plymouth harbour all that time.

Lord Howard is in charge of all of the English ships and we are to sail behind his ship, the Ark Royal, if ever the Armada comes that is!

This is Lord Charles Howard who is to lead the English fleet out to meet the Spanish.

There is a lot of sickness on board the ships. Lord Howard's own fleet off Cattewater has fever aboard and Thomas told me that the soldiers have orders to kill anyone who tries to jump ship and run away. It must be awful for them. We have no sickness on the Disdain, Uncle Edward makes us keep the ship too clean for that. We all have to stay on board, though, so that we can leave as soon as the beacon is lit and the orders given.

Uncle Edward is keeping us all busy with sail changes. He says it will save our lives in the battle. Thomas has been working with the Gunners and I haven't had much chance to speak to him. I wanted to help him fire the cannon but Uncle Edward wouldn't let me. He said I was to stick to my own jobs and do them properly!

1588

July 19

At last the Armada has been sighted. Captain Fleming took the news to the commanders who were playing a game of bowls on the Hoe at the time. I wished I had been there. They

My friends tell me that Sir Francis Drake was playing a game of bowls on the Hoe when the Armada was sighted.

say that Sir Francis Drake was winning and refused to stop the game. He said there was plenty of time to finish the game and beat the Spanish! The whole fleet is talking about it. He was right though, for the tide was against us and we have had to wait for it to turn before any of the fleet can sail out. We may not even be able to get out then because the wind is strongly against us. I always carry my dagger with me now. I keep it tucked in my belt.

Uncle Edward had us make ready to sail as soon as the news came. That's the order to raise anchor now!

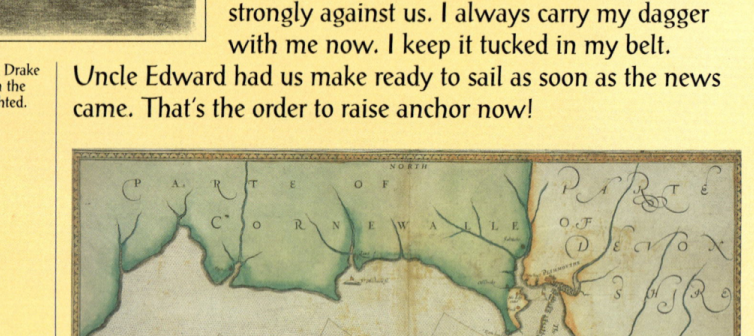

This tapestry shows the crescent-shaped battle formation used by the Spanish Armada.

July 21

So much has happened that I don't know if I can write it all down and it is not over yet.

We finally got out of harbour and headed due south with Lord Howard's fleet. When we first saw the mighty Spanish Armada it filled us with awe. There were hundreds of ships all close together in the shape of a huge crescent moon. The largest galleons were protecting the smaller ships. Lord Howard sent signals for us to line up to the right and behind the Armada and Drake's fleet came round from the other side.

1588

For a while nothing happened. It was awful just waiting. I got really scared then. At last we got a message from the Ark Royal. Lord Howard had chosen our ship, the Disdain, to fire the first cannon shot at the Armada!

We edged out of the heaving ships that lay all around us and sailed out alone across the water. Uncle Edward gave orders for the Gunners to load and Thomas set his men to work pressing down the powder into the barrels of the cannon and loading the shot. We turned sideways on. We were so close that I could see the Spanish men on their galleons. It made me feel all mixed up, sort of excited but at the same time really frightened.

Uncle Edward nodded to Thomas and he gave the signal to fire. It was a terrible noise. The smoke and the smell of burning powder stung my throat and made me choke.

Our shots fell short and I thought that would be the end of us. I was sure they would all fire at us and we would sink, but they didn't and we returned to our place in the English fleet – much to my relief!

1588

After that the attack began. It was very difficult to know what was happening. Uncle Edward had enough trouble just trying to steer between the other English ships without crashing into them, let alone fire shots at the Spanish. All through the battle Uncle Edward stayed at the helm. He was so calm and still that we all felt steadied, but his face was grim. I would not have crossed him for anything. Nothing seemed to stop the Spanish. They just kept on going up the Channel. All we could do was follow them with the rest of the fleet.

After the firing stopped I was violently sick and had a terrible headache. Thomas said that he was sick, too, after his first fight at sea. I tried not to show how much I was shaking but I think some of the men knew. Uncle Edward sent me below to check for damage to the hull and I felt better down there alone and in the dark.

It is now night and we have hung lanterns on the prow and stern so that we can be seen by the other ships. I don't think I can sleep. Who knows what will happen to us tomorrow. We must stop the Spanish. We just must!

1588

July 28

There have been running battles up the Channel now for more than a week. Our water and food supplies are very low and have to be rationed. Every one of the crew is exhausted. It just never ends. I dare not say it but I don't think the Armada can be stopped, not now they have come so far.

Only Drake has had some success. Word got to us a week ago that he captured a big Spanish galleon called the Rosario. I cheered when I heard but Uncle Edward just raised his eyebrows and said nothing.

Here you can see the English and the Spanish ships in battle.

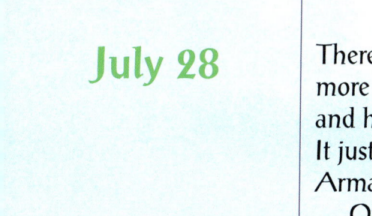

One of our Gunners was hurt in the last fight. I have to help look after him. Thomas has taken his place firing the cannon. I hope he will be alright.

The Captains have all been rowed over to the Ark Royal to a meeting with Lord Howard. The Armada ships have gone into Calais harbour because of the gales. We have dropped anchor outside the harbour and we must wait for our next orders. I hope Uncle Edward comes back on board soon. I don't feel safe without him.

1588

July 29

It was terrible. Fire ships were sent into Calais harbour in the middle of the night. As the Spanish tried to escape from the fires, our ships shot at them. It went on all night and by dawn the Spanish fleet was scattered. Lord Seymour's fleet joined up with our ships this morning and, as the Spanish ships tried to re-group, we attacked them.

The battle was awful. Ships seemed to be crashing into each other. Cannon shot was being fired all around us. The noise was deafening and it never stopped. Everywhere I looked, ships were on fire and sinking. Men were screaming and jumping overboard, even though they couldn't swim.

Our mainsails were ripped and the foremast broken by cannon fire from one of the Spanish ships. Two of the crew were crushed when the mast broke and fell. They're dead. Almost at once we seemed to catch a wave badly and the ship nearly sank. It was at that moment that I thought we were all going to die.

1588

Thomas and all the Gunners kept on firing. I was trying to lower the foresails when one of the cannon seemed to explode backwards. As the smoke cleared, I realised that it was the one Thomas had been firing. I don't remember how I got there but somehow I reached Thomas. He was lying half under the ripped and twisted metal of the gun. He was covered in black powder and his skin was raw with burns. He made no sound or movement. I pulled and pulled at his shoulders to drag him free of the gun. Someone helped me but I don't know who. All I kept saying was 'He can't be dead. He mustn't be dead.' I shook him as hard as I could to make him wake up but he wouldn't.

Suddenly my uncle's voice stopped me. 'Will!' he said, very close to me, 'Stand back.' I must have stood up because I remember looking down at Thomas. Uncle Edward had a bucket of sea water in his hand and he drenched Thomas. It seemed to me that everything had gone quiet. The battle must have been going on but I didn't hear it or see it. All I cared about was Thomas. My uncle knelt down and felt Thomas' head. As he touched the bit that was bleeding Thomas seemed to jerk and groan. He didn't open his eyes but I knew, I knew he was alive.

I must have shut my eyes for a moment because when I looked at him again Uncle Edward was helping him to sit up a little. I went to hold him but my uncle held me back and although I struggled I knew I wouldn't get past him. He turned to me and told me to leave Thomas for a while. I had to do what he said. Thomas was carried below. His leg was bleeding badly and I think it was broken.

1588

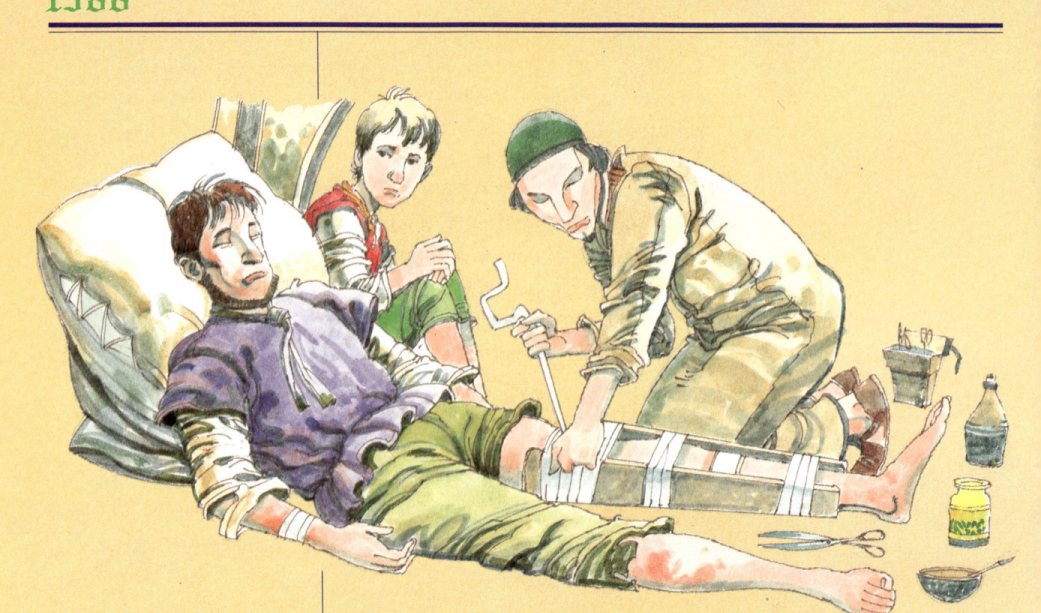

I wasn't allowed to go to him until after we had limped out of the battle area and into Calais harbour for repairs. He looked in pain and his breathing was shallow. I crept alongside him and sat watching him. He opened his eyes and tried to smile but the burns on his face hurt him too much. His leg was pulled straight between two planks of wood and it was tied tightly. His hands, neck and face were burned and his head cut. I hoped and prayed he would live.

This is the kind of jar that the physician used to hold the medicine.

As I sat there, Uncle Edward came down with a physician from town. My uncle spoke to him in French. I had to move out of the way to let the man look at Thomas but my uncle didn't send me away. The physician gave Thomas something to drink from a small bottle. He checked the leg which hurt Thomas and then tied it again. I didn't understand what he said to my uncle but he gave him the bottle and some salve in a flat pot. My uncle paid him and they both went on deck.

Uncle Edward came back just as I was moving my bedding so that I could sleep nearer to Thomas. He told me that the drink would help take away the pain and the salve was for the burns. The leg, he said, would heal straight if Thomas kept still. He said I could help look after Thomas as long as I did my other jobs. I must have smiled because he smiled back although I could see how tired he was. I don't want to go to war again.

1588

August 4

We sailed into Plymouth today. There were lots of people at the quayside and they all cheered. Thomas was carried up to see it all. It is strange but I didn't feel good about it. I just felt tired and I wanted to go home to sleep. Thomas is staying with us until he can walk again. The news is all over Plymouth. The Armada is beaten. I'm glad but I wish I felt better. Uncle Edward understands. He sent me to bed straight after supper. I am going to sleep for ever. Thank God it is over.

These special medals are being given to the brave seamen who helped to defeat the Armada.

August 22

It's nearly three weeks since we came back from the battle. It seems ages ago now. The Disdain is ready to sail again. We've heard no more of the Spanish although the town is full of talk. They say that Drake sails back to Plymouth and will be here soon. I wish I could be here to see that but I can't because we are to sail on the noon tide. I do hope the weather stays fair and there are no storms!

Glossary

Armada A fleet of warships. In this case, sent by the Spanish.

Beacon A bundle of twigs and straw mounted on a large pole which was lit as a signal of invasion. The beacons were placed on high points of land and within sight of one another. As one was lit so the rest followed on. It was the quickest way of communicating danger before the arrival of the telegraph or telephone.

Boatswain A ship's officer in charge of sails.

Bowls A competitive game involving the rolling of balls over a flat lawn to get as close to a small white ball (the jack), as possible.

Cadiz A coastal town that was in Spanish territory in 1588 and now is part of Portugal.

Calais A French port on the Channel.

Cannon A weapon of war, made of metal, using gunpowder to throw cannon balls at the enemy, with a view to damaging walls or ship's sides and masts.

Canvas A material which is coarse and strong, used for sails and coverings.

Cattewater The name of a piece of land opposite Plymouth harbour.

Catholic Belonging to the Catholic religion, a Christian faith which has the Pope as its leader.

Cherbourg A French sea port on the Channel.

Doublet A close fitting jacket, often made of leather, worn in Elizabethan times.

Fire boats Small ships deliberately set alight with burning pitch and sent into enemy ships to set them alight.

First Mate The second in command on a ship, deputy to the Ship's Master.

Flask A small narrow-necked bottle, often carried in a pocket.

Fleet A large group of ships brought together to fight and controlled by one commander.

Foresails The small sails used on the foremast – the mast at the front of the ship.

Galleon A large warship of the Elizabethan times, with sails and a high wooden castle-like structure at the back of the ship. They were usually Spanish and had many cannon.

Helm The place on a ship where the steering equipment is found.

Hoe A flattish piece of rough ground at the top of the cliff which rises above Plymouth.

Hose In Elizabethan times this word meant the breeches or short trousers that the men used to wear.

Hull The wooden shell of the ship.

Mainsail The large centre sail used on the mainmast.

Master The man who ran the ship during Elizabethan times and often owned it. He would also navigate. He does the job that a captain does today.

Master Gunner The man in charge of looking after and firing the cannon on board ship.

Powder In the diary this refers to gunpowder, used to fire cannon.

Protestant A member of a religious group that broke away from the beliefs and practices of the Catholic Church in the sixteenth century, following the beliefs of Martin Luther.

Prow The front of the ship.

Rigging Ropes used to support the sails and masts.

Ship's Boy A boy employed on the ship to do all the jobs that needed someone small, agile and light, sometimes climbing the rigging. It was a way of learning the craft of seamanship but it was very hard and they often had to do the worst jobs.

Sound A stretch of water in front of Plymouth harbour which is sheltered by the land on either side.

Spar A sturdy pole, at right angles to the mast, from which sails hang.

Spent In the diary this means used up.

Stern The back end of a ship.

Tanner A person whose job is to treat raw cow hides to make leather.

Topsail A sail above the rest of the sails on the mast.

Treason A crime against the monarch or country, usually involving a plot to overthrow them or kill them. It is still punishable by death.

Twelfth Night The last night of the 12 days of Christmas that finish with the Feast of the Epiphany 6 January. At this time it was the custom to give presents on this night rather than on Christmas Day.